THE
BULLIED
BREED

My Story of Salvation from the Pit Bull Stigma

THE
BULLIED
BREED

My Story of Salvation from the Pit Bull Stigma

Peeta

Co-author/Transcriber: Jennifer Foy Schalhoub
Collaborator: Paul Schalhoub

DEDICATION

This book is dedicated to
my beloved humans.

We may not be connected by birth,
but we are related through Mother Earth.
We were created; our paths became one.
There is no mistaking that I am your sun.

What do you call it when
someone is filled with love
but always misunderstood?

Such a *Pittie*!

TABLE OF CONTENTS

PREFACE

Sit…now, stay!

Good reader. I am delighted that you have chosen to em*bark* upon this journey with me! I write and you read—good trade. (More accurately: I dictate, my human types, then eventually you read.) I have tried typing myself. It's fun, but not very productive. When I attempt to press one key, my paw hits all the surrounding ten. This results in an indecipherable narrative that takes way too much time to decode.

PEETA

Let me begin by saying that I never thought I'd write a book. Then again, so much of life is never what we thought it would be...have you noticed that? That's why it's so important to be open to every opportunity that comes your way. Of course, having started this project, I worry every day that I may have bitten off more than I can chew. But I've never met anything I couldn't chew. So, onward and upward. As confident as I am in my human's ability to translate, if anything is unclear or ambiguous, just ask your dog to explain it to you. I do realize that not everyone has a dog to help them, but you can ask anyone's dog. (Just don't ask a cat. They have a wickedly funny habit of intentionally paraphrasing things incorrectly in order to witness the fallout. Clever little rascals.)

PREFACE

One last thing…if I seem a little unrefined at times, please forgive me. In order to survive on the streets, one must adopt the air of a scrappy mutt. I may not be well read or well bred, but all that you hear will be very sincere.

CHAPTER ONE:
DELIVER US FROM EVIL

"To err is human;
to forgive, divine."
~ Alexander Pope

If I may be so bold, I prefer...to err is human; to forgive, canine. I do hope someone quotes ME one day. Anyway, as far as I can tell, the divine trait of forgiveness was not inherently gifted to the human species. They try, but they struggle. We dogs, on the other hand, are forgiving to a fault, like when we maintain a level of loyalty to those who mistreat us. Throughout history, the canine class has upheld its duty to do as it was told. And so, the *pittie*ful truth is that Pit Bulls who are unable to shed their manipulated behaviors are really only doing unto others as was done unto them.

It has only been in recent years that humans have been held accountable for negatively shaping our behavior purely to benefit their own needs. Add to that the practices used to enhance that behavior...unthinkable. Such cruelty may incur a punishment whereby the human offender is given a sentence with an end date. Therein lies the painful disparity: the Pit Bull stigma has no expiration date. We've been branded for life after life after life…you get the idea. The damage is done, figuratively and literally.

The reason we look scary is because we were designed to instill fear…and worse. It's right there in the name. The "pit" is not exactly a playpen, and believe me, there is no winner. Aside from the obvious horror, another consequence is that the top dog in a fight becomes the underdog in a shelter. And I can tell you from experience it's not much fun being treated like last week's trash, being moved around until someone finally disposes of you.

And since dogs are in no way concerned with appearances, it's difficult for us to wrap our brains around any such affectations. Humans, on the other paw, can be quite preoccupied with the outward display. This makes it even more challenging for those of us who don't fit the right profile.

Thus, in defense of all those who are misrepresented, prejudged, under-appreciated, and overlooked, I set forth this account with *dogged* determination.

I hope that my story will inspire more people to take *Pittie*!

Paws crossed.

CHAPTER TWO:
A FEW MINOR
ALTERATIONS

As much as we dogs like to approach things from the rear (end), I'll start at the very beginning.

North Carolina is a distant memory and a big blur. I was very young and had no point of reference for, well, anything. One day I was just there, aware of my puppyhood in a litter that was viewed as no more than litter. Somehow I acquired a few small scars, a complete lack of social etiquette, and I become apoplectic whenever I'm indoors with a fly. But for the most part I remained intact; I say "for the most part" because I still don't know what happened to my balls.

It's no secret that I'm a Pit Dalmatian mix (which parent was which is not apparent), and it turns out this variety is quite unique. I'm fine with no degree of pedigree, but please be assured that I'm an honorable mongrel. Being of good canine character is more important than a lofty lineage.

But throw in the preconceptions about the Dalmatian temperament, and I wasn't exactly in contention for dog of the week. With a Pittie head that was way too big for my extremely underweight Dalmatian body, the comment I heard most often was, "What IS that?"

I'd like to give a shout out to the genius that came up with the label Pit Bull. Thanks for the gift that keeps on giving. (It's not like we voluntarily joined Fight Club.) And how typical that when similar circumstances were inflicted on humans, they were given the admirable title of Gladiator. Instead of Pit Bull I propose Cheeky Monkey. As one of my nicknames, it certainly captures the essence of our natural sass and humor, not to mention our unmistakable bone structure.

I'm so thankful I got to keep my ears—my full ears. I've been told that my left ear flops up and down when I trot, and for some reason this brings intense delight to my humans.

Another thing about ears—when I'm listening, I'm all ears. But when I sense my humans approaching for a cuddle, I can make my ears completely disappear! That's known as dolphin head, and it's a specialty with Pitties.

My most vivid memory from my first year was the day my balls disappeared. According to my medical papers, I was about one year old. You know how sometimes you just can't find that specific toy? You know you had it, but it's nowhere to be found? Eventually it shows up in a sneaker or some such place. Well, this was, by far, the weirdest disappearing act I've ever witnessed.

I remember being contained in a crate and feeling very anxious, but somehow I fell into a solid sleep. Upon awakening, I felt very groggy and disoriented…but not so much so that I would misplace my balls! I had always kept them in the same place, without exception. So, you can imagine my surprise when I went to clean them and they were GONE. I do mean GONE. As in NOT THERE. Thoroughly perplexed, I looked everywhere. I retraced my steps as best I could in the place where I was staying at the time, but nothing. No hint, no trace, no balls. It was very disconcerting to think that while I was sleeping someone had stolen them.

But here's the crazy part—turns out I didn't need 'em! Over a short period of time, I completely forgot about them. Literally. And my undercarriage became a lot less complcated, truth be told. No danglers, no knick knacks, no dice. Just a clean swath of speckled fur. Of course, my didgeridoo takes center stage now, and that's absolutely fine. Nobody abducted HIM, which is very convenient because he serves a very important function. Every day, when I'm out and about, I have to lift my leg so he can say hello to all his friends: the trees, the bushes, the hydrants. He's very popular.

Speaking of lost jewels, I fully support the spay/neuter movement...more spay, fewer stray. Kind of a no brainer, don't you think? Yeah, it is for those of us who are born onto concrete,

and into the most dangerous circumstances imaginable, especially if
you're a breed nobody wants. But
humans sometimes don't get that
they have the means by which to
really help the overpopulation problem. There are the enlightened ones
who try to spread the word, and it
does move the cause in the right
direction, but more people need to
get on board. Also, don't feel uncomfortable if you get spay and neuter
confused. I've heard many humans
hesitate and still get them mixed up.
For the record—a female dog is
spayed, and a male dog is neutered.

But I think I know why some humans
don't understand the importance of
removing the spawn feature. Whenever I'm out, I see stray humans all
over the place, wandering around,
nobody walking them. They're

completely loose and unsupervised. And other humans (who belong to dogs) don't seem alarmed! My humans don't try to catch these stray humans, but I have noticed we move away from them as quickly as possible. It's as if, for humans, concerns about reproduction aren't a priority. Well, they should be! My nose tells me that all these stray people aren't fixed, and last I checked mankind has a bit of an overpopulation problem as well.

CHAPTER THREE:
THE STATE I'M IN

The plane ride from North Carolina to New Jersey was so terrifying that I can't adequately put it into words. I do believe I shall never recover. Even though my humans didn't know me then, they believe that ordeal could be the reason for my "issues" in the house. If the water pipes rattle or bang, if the washing machine swooshes, if the dryer hums, pots and pans ping, and—worst of all—if a ceiling fan whirls, I have a very bad time of it. Thankfully, my humans don't use the ceiling fans anymore, and they go out of their way to shield me from the other terrors. I'm getting better.

In spite of surviving that plane ride, I quickly concluded that flying is not for dogs. And yet that challenging journey was a pivotal experience in my ultimate transformation.

The landing of the plane was so shocking that I may have lost consciousness. After being unloaded, it took a long time for me to trust the ground. And what was the point of such panic? The surrounding area where we landed looked identical to the place we had left. There were so many of those frightful planes that I couldn't breathe properly until we left in a land vehicle. I had been scared the first time I traveled in a car, but after air travel, the land vehicle seemed like a magic carpet ride. I gathered from what I was hearing that now I was in New Jersey.

Please know that I never intend to offend, but if I may be brutally honest, "New" Jersey didn't look very new. If I had to hazard a guess, I'd say it was settled at least 15 years ago, maybe even more. Anyway, I was deposited in a new place that had lots of dogs to play with, which was great because I was starved for friendly canine com-panionship. Unfortunately, I was a bit too exuberant in my encounters, and the end result for me was isolation. Everyone kept saying that I didn't play well with others...something about not knowing his own strength. I heard that so many times I began to wonder, "Why doesn't someone

21

introduce me to His Own Strength, since he seems to know so much about appropriate play?"

Isolation was the worst. It made me miserable and anxious. Instead of realizing that frenzied play would lead to loneliness, I just figured every moment of joy was followed by a spell of gloom. I hadn't experienced enough moments of joy to differentiate. Thus far, my life had been nothing more than a series of changes: no routine, no constants, no positive reinforcement. I liked this new location better than where I'd been before, but everyone was so busy. Understandably, nobody really had much time for me.

The humans in this new place were really nice to me, but I could not understand what was going on. Every now and then they'd bring me into a room to meet some newer humans. I'd be so afraid that I'd hide behind a chair, and the visitors were instructed not to make eye contact. As you can imagine, after each of these meetings, I would never see those humans again. Since these encounters never seemed to go very well, I couldn't fathom why we kept having them. But at least it was less depressing than solitary.

One particular day (a Tuesday), I was feeling really down, more so than usual. I was hungry, lonely, and hoping someone would spend some time with me. When they led me to the meeting room that evening, my sense of dread and disappointment was very heavy. I thought, "Here we go again."

But this time, when I entered the room, something was different. I couldn't put my paw on it, but the atmosphere in the room was unlike it had ever been before. Instead of dissatisfaction, disappointment, and rejection, there was a feeling of calm acceptance, curiosity, and warmth.

I hadn't been fed that day, and now I knew why. My favorite treats were on the table, and they were going to be given by these new humans—a man and a woman. All three of us tried not to make eye contact, but each of us kept stealing a glance and then pretending we hadn't. My desire to hide was not as strong as usual, but I suppose I did it out of habit. The woman seemed delighted with the encounter and, in her excitement, excused herself to go pee. (I wish I could have gone out to pee.) Finding it easier to focus on one at a time, I came out from behind the chair and moved slowly toward the man. He was sitting on the floor, holding a treat very near to his lap. As I leaned in to take it, he stretched his neck out toward me, and I suddenly found myself close to his face. What was I to do? I could only think of one thing—I kissed him. He was very proud, and everyone made a happy fuss. But when the woman came back from wherever she had peed, she looked disappointed and wanted to know what she had missed.

Upon learning that I had kissed him, the woman had an expression that I shall never forget. She looked sad. Genuinely sad. Like she had missed something incredible. I had never seen anyone react that way toward something that I had done. I could literally feel her spirit shift; that first kiss mattered deeply to her, and she had missed it. This development confused me further. Most humans I had offered a kiss to didn't want it. I asked myself, "Should I do it again?" I wasn't near the man anymore, and with no treat being offered, my sudden advance could be misinterpreted. (To date, my actions had been constantly misinterpreted, and that's one of the reasons I felt so uncomfortable around those I didn't know.) But something else was happening...to MY spirit. In that moment, I found myself desperately wanting to make this woman happy. I imagined kissing her face for long periods of time. Again, my confusion deepened. I needed to snap out of this funk because these humans were going to leave, and I would never see them again. There was no upside to having thoughts that would torment me during solitary.

As expected, they left. The next few days were as disjointed as ever. I didn't know whom I'd see, who was scheduled to check on me, who would come, and who would go. I had made a few canine friends, but they kept disappearing, usually after one of those visitor meetings. I found myself wishing I had not seen that couple. I couldn't stop thinking about them, and it was bothering me. I didn't know why; it felt like something was incomplete. Why was that woman so dejected simply because she missed me kissing the man? Was my kiss that important? I would never know.

By Friday, things had become increasingly odd. Everyone was acting differently. I had a super long bath (which I hated), and a lot of attention and conversation was focused in my direction. I didn't know what to make of it. I was getting kind of nervous, and I began to fear that I'd be put on that horrible, airborne contraption again. Please, NO. Not that.

Instead, what happened next was surreal. I hope I can aptly depict the awe-inspiring events of that evening because it was the most important day of my life. I was sitting in my lonely space, wondering how long it would be before I could get dirty again, when I heard voices. I kind of recognized them, but I couldn't place them. I tilted my head. I tilted it more.

It was that couple.

They had come back.

CHAPTER FOUR: SERENDIPITTIE

As far as I'm concerned, the day I was adopted may as well have been the day I was born. I experienced a singular, overwhelming sentiment; it was essential that I go with THAT man and THAT woman. Emotionally, it felt nonnegotiable...in the way that physically breathing is nonnegotiable.

Lots of paperwork, and quite a bit of fuss over the last name of the vet who treated me in North Carolina. Turns out it was the same last name as MY woman's maiden name. Had she been a maid? Does one have to change one's name as a maid? I still don't understand why that was relevant, but it's still a topic of conversation to this day, usually told with genuine amazement. (I'm always respectful and pretend to be interested.)

The people that were handing me over to MY humans seemed very happy to be giving me away but heartbroken to see me go. Does that make any sense? Kooky humans. Out we walked into the beautiful May air with me sporting a brand new harness as I walked MY humans for the first time. Then we arrived at the car…

If only I had a video of these two dears trying to get me into the car that first evening. What idiots they were. First they tried to lure me in with treats. Then they took turns getting in the back seat and inviting me. Then one sat in the front and one in the back, holding the leash. Then they switched. Passersby were stop--ping, laughing, taking photos, making suggestions. Oh, the drama! My humans strategized, they analyzed, they went out of their way trying not to terrorize. I did admire them for not wanting to scare me right off the bat, but it went on for quite some time. FINALLY, and ever so gently, the man lifted me in his arms and placed me in the back seat up against the woman. I tried, I really tried, to give him a look that said, "Why didn't you just do that in the first place?" But he missed it because he was looking joyfully into the eyes of the woman who was cooing and crying all at once. He got into the driver's seat and off we went, driving towards my new life and future.

I can't really say how long we were in that car that first evening because I fell asleep within five minutes. I was leaning against the woman, trying to be respectful of her personal space. She was going out of her way to make it clear that her personal space was mine for the taking. Her encouragement was so convincing that I ended up accepting the invitation, collapsing into her lap, and passing out.

My first night, in what was to become MY house, was a bit nerve wracking. Here I found myself in the coziest place I'd ever been with no inkling of how to behave. I was beyond exhausted, so picking up clues was extremely difficult. I kept waking up with nightmares, which seemed more like memories, and then I would wonder where I was for the first several seconds. My greatest fear was realized when I felt my sphincter muscle lose consciousness. I knew my nerves had blended everything they'd fed me into a liquid mélange of horrors, and I was about to let loose in this lovely couple's nest. I made the one smart move I could think of; I ran for the floor that wasn't carpeted. What emerged from inside me was unlike anything I had ever seen before. Let's just leave it at that.

I wondered if this turn of events might cause my humans to observe me in a new light. But do you know what? It was all praise for choosing the hard floor and compassion for how ill I must be feeling. "Who ARE these people who wouldn't hit, scold, or repel me?" I asked myself. It was as if they KNEW I wouldn't have done it if I could have helped it.

That was the moment I made the most incredible realization. These two humans were my Mom and Dad. MY Mom and Dad. I had finally found them. I was still pondering this revelation when I fell into the deepest sleep I have ever experienced.

I couldn't have known it at the time, but I woke up the next day into a whole new identity. It only took a few days to get used to my new name, Peeta, but my new responsibilities were deeply transforming over time. I don't know what was better, discovering what these assignments were or carrying them out. I'm still enjoying that part!

SERENDIPITTIE

According to my yearly review, I've been improving in leaps and bounds.

Literally. Leaps and bounds.

CHAPTER FIVE: DISCOVERY

This was me before I found Mom and Dad. I don't like to think back on those days much. Luckily, we dogs don't dwell on the past. We tend to live in the moment—a critical skill that seems to elude many humans.

Photo Courtesy of See Spot Rescued

For months, every time I woke up I would momentarily panic in fear that it was all a dream. But then I would look over at Mom and Dad, each clinging to their respective patch of the mattress while I enjoyed the center swath. Sometimes I would go right back to sleep after a good stretch and a deep sigh. Other times I'd just stare at them while they slept. I still do that. I will always do that.

During that first year in my new home I encountered so many firsts it was hard to keep track. The word overwhelming comes to mind, but that's not to say I couldn't handle it. As if having a home were not enough of a blessing, I was taken on trips during which I thought my nose would fall right off my face. The variety of smells made me delirious. Every day was exhilarating, and every night I would collapse in exhaustion.

I would now like to recount some of those firsts (for purely selfish reasons, of course).

Do all the other states know that New Jersey has this stuff on the ground called grass? Maybe that's why it's called the Garden State. All I can say is I don't know how I lived without it. At first it freaked me out; it would tickle, irritate, and hurt my paws all at once. I would try to get to pavement as fast as I could. But after my instincts had a chance to engage, and my paws understood the sensation, and I realized that grass grows upward from soil...OMG! Now I literally can't get enough. I roll in it, sleep in it, dig down into it, eat it. I LOVE IT!

As for my first encounter with water, it was literally a sink or swim initiation. My humans were there, but I discovered the doggy paddle very quickly indeed! And now? Pond, stream, river, lake, ocean—yup, all mine. And don't even get me started on coming out of the ocean and rolling with abandon in the sand. I get goose bumps just thinking about it.

One of our favorite vacation spots is Cape May, New Jersey. Mom says I gallop like a horse, so she found a rental unit with an entire acre for my galloping enjoyment and an entire ocean for my swimming pleasure. It's so bizarre, this ocean thing. It moves by ITSELF, and it's filled with salt and sand. It's quite different from the river, which has no salt (good), rocks instead of sand (bad), and the water goes in only one direction (scary). There is also a major retrieval differential between the ocean and the river. At the beach, if I can't get my stick in time, the motion of the ocean politely returns it to me! But the rude river will just take my stick from me faster than I can swim. My humans start screaming and they pull me back in on my leash. It is SO embarrassing, especially if there are other dogs around. Go figure, with all those rocks, there's never one big enough to crawl under.

My favorite, however, was my first encounter with snow. It truly and completely blew my mind. Soft, chilled powder falling from the sky, gathering on the ground, getting deeper and deeper. I could jump into the air to catch it as it fell. I could dive into drifts of it and take the ultimate chill pill. I could run in circles and slip, slide, swivel, and skate. When it got really deep, a tossed toy would completely disappear, and I'd have to go in on a reconnaissance mission. Oh, the joy! Where had this gift from above been before now? How could I have missed it? It was one of the most beautiful miracles I had ever seen. Then, when I grasped the concept that it would happen repeatedly, randomly, every year during the coldest months…well, my head nearly exploded. On snow days, I really AM Snow Dog. And may it always be so.

Snow or grass? Hot or cold? Which do I prefer? How lucky am I to even ponder the contrast in terms of a preference? I wish all dogs could escape indoors when the elements are not to their liking. But I digress, as always, into the unsettling imbalance between fortune and misfortune.

My deep sense of gratitude usually directs my thoughts back to the hardships of less fortunate dogs. Mom suffers from this distraction terribly; sometimes we get melancholy together, and we just snuggle up tight and wish for a better world. Mom's tears are salty. If only more humans were kind. I mean, it's right there in the name...man*kind*. Sort of in the same way that the word humane is comprised mostly of the word *human*.

I wish that every tale could have a happy ending, and that every tail could BE a happy ending—a satisfied, wiggling caboose.

Oh, dear. Now I've really lost this thread. I *stray* so far off the mark; I'm going to try to follow the scent back to the original point.

Oh! Winter or summer! I've noticed that the summer sun drains me, but the winter sun invigorates me. So that's one point for cold. I love grass and snow for different reasons, but frolicking in the snow is the only time I don't have to worry about gnats, flies, and ticks (and even that guideline is shifting). And boy, do I hate ticks. You never want to be the host with the most; they're nasty little buggers, and they will feast on any beast. Pay attention to every *tick*le and have no mercy.

So, fewer ticks—that's another point for winter. Well, my humans prefer the cold, so I guess I'd choose winter. But since grass, soil, sand, and water are so freakishly awesome, I hope we always stay in this place that gives us a rotating variety. Do the other states know that New Jersey not only has grass, but also a proverbial buffet of seasons? I know New York caught on to the concept, but the other states should really check it out.

Ah, the beach! Maybe I like the warm weather better...

I got it! Whatever season I'm enjoying at any given moment is my favorite. (I've been spending so much time in the company of humans that sometimes I have to consciously engage my canine mindset. Live in the moment.)

Now on to the joys of dog play dates. I'd like to clear up one major misconception. All the humans think a dog park is a playground for a play date. But we hounds know it's all about netwerking. Think about it. We are all fenced in, there's safety in numbers, and it's easy to get lost in a crowd. It's the perfect venue for a run, a jump, a hump, and a dump.

And another thing! Why do humans put such a derogatory spin on "being anal?" We dogs swear by it; in fact, it's often how a meet and greet begins. It's just common canine courtesy. I'd go so far as to say we put the "anal" in "analysis." You're welcome.

The next eye opener for me was the art of contact. I love a good massage, and Dad gives the best on the planet. But get this! I heard that humans go to a place called a spa where they pay other humans to massage them. I wish I could explain to them that they don't have to pay. Just go in, wiggle your butt, roll on the floor, and show them your tummy. Mom and Dad tried to explain to me that, as humans, such behavior would get you one of three things: arrested, put in a straight jacket, or rewarded with a different type of massage. Humans are so complicated.

Regardless, when it comes to one's muscles, any dog worth his salt knows that the best way to loosen up is to roll your own *joints*.

DISCOVERY

CHAPTER SIX:
RENAISSANCE MAN

Two things I fell in love with immediately upon adoption: ice hockey and the music of the band Rush. It was easy, but I have a scary feeling it might have been a requirement. (Happy to report that, once I came on board, hockey and Rush had to sit behind me on the priority bus.) I was incorporated into the family during hockey playoffs, so it was nothing BUT hockey. I know a thing or two about rough play turning into a fight, hurling my body, and being condemned to the penalty box. But those silly hockey players just don't get it...sticks should always be carried in the mouth.

As for Rush, what's not to love? For those of you who picked up on my reference to Snow Dog, you will also understand why I wag my tail every time I'm told to "Leave That Thing Alone." And you'll love this! It is estimated by the vet in North Carolina that I was born in November 2012. So my humans took it upon themselves to declare my date of birth as November 21st. Wait for it... 11/21/12. All you Rushians will approve. I am the Alpha Canis Majoris, and I have assumed control.

Speaking of names, in North Carolina my name was That One. Very confusing. But it's probably because nobody was ever speaking TO me; they were just speaking ABOUT me. At the rescue group in Jersey City, New Jersey, my name was Bruno Mars. I think all the dogs were given famous names in order to make them more memorable and more easily identifiable. They probably chose that name for me because I have a beautiful singing voice. (Or so I'm told.)

I now know that the three names vying for my new identity were: Tuukka, Doc, and Peeta. Hockey fans may recognize Tuukka, an incredible goalie from Finland. No need to explain that choice. Doc, after Mike Emerick, of course. He's an all-things-hockey guru, and a loyal dog lover/advocate/champion. In the end, though, Peeta was the one. (Duh! I realize you probably determined that already.) It's from a book called *The Hunger Games* by Suzanne Collins. The character somehow manages to preserve his purely good and loving nature in spite of all the damage that is done to him. Mom said if ever a name fit…

Of all the gifts granted to me, one of the easiest to fall in love with was country life. My favorite thing is sleeping outdoors and communicating with the coyotes. When I say outdoors, I mean a screened in porch. My humans fret because the only thing between me and all the wildlife and activity during the night is an exhausted screen in an antiquated house. When the coyotes begin their high-pitched yelps, yips, and yowls, I start howling back. Even though we speak different dialects, it's always a pleasant exchange. They invite me to walk on the wild side, and I explain that I would love to but would never leave my humans to fend for themselves. The coyotes are quite understanding. Although, I think they are baffled by the routine of my life. Or rather, by my satisfaction with it.

During our most recent visit, the coyotes were the closest they've ever been. It was very exhilarating, but my humans looked quite terrified. I forgot that even though my humans understand ME, perhaps they are not able to translate the language of my relatives. Add to that the exhausted screen in the antiquated house, and I suppose they had good reason to be alarmed.

Eventually the ancestral pack (or is that wolves?) moved on. My humans went back to sleep, but I could not. I started thinking about my genealogy. Have you ever heard of 23andMe? I'm not sure exactly how many coyotes there were that night, but it seemed like 23 (and me).

Did you know that peepers are tiny little frogs? I had never heard them, or heard of them, until I began visiting the country. They conduct an orchestra during the spring, from dusk until well into the night. The sound is beautiful, hypnotizing, and sometimes deafening. Each little frog has their own miniature squeaky toy, and they all go at it simultaneously. Most incredibly, I've heard them all come to a complete stop at the same exact second. How the hell do they manage that? When I'm down by the pond, which is like their bar where they hang out, I've often tried to engage them in conversation, so I can ask them questions. But they never seem to want to talk to me. In fact, they scoot away in the blink of an eye. (I bet they're afraid I'll steal their toys and spread their performance secrets.)

Did you know there is a difference between sound and noise? I've made a very interesting observation. Mom likes QUIET. I mean dead silence. But the sounds that are made by birds, frogs, dogs, coyotes, wind, rain, you name it...she loves those. (I think I am beginning to understand what organic means.) I wonder how she squares that with all the times she and Dad blew out their eardrums at Rush concerts. Then again, Rush music is so smooth and uncompromising that it actually feels organic.

I have discovered that there's a learning curve with everything, so I try not to be too hard on myself. On one occasion my humans left me behind to travel on one of those terrifying airplane contraptions, and I was like, "See ya!" Absolutely true. I didn't want anything to do with that trip, but I was a complete wreck when they left me. But will wonders never cease? I stayed with a lovely lady, I had a dog companion the entire time, and after my initial shock at being forsaken, I actually made out just fine. I'd go so far as to say it was borderline fascinating. Hustle and bustle, with me in constant investigative mode.

Do I prefer trips that my humans and I can experience together? Absolutely. Did I miss them that week? Without question. But I managed. Turns out the one who has separation anxiety is...can you guess? Of course it's Mom! When we're apart she doesn't handle it very well, and when we're reunited I don't know which one of us is happier. I wiggle, wag, and warble while she just falls apart.

After much thought, I have come to this conclusion:

Whether you're the human
or whether you're the hound,
separately you're lost,
but together you are found.

Full disclosure: Extensive homecoming celebrations occur even if Mom just goes out to buy milk.

CHAPTER SEVEN:
JOB DESCRIPTION

I am never derelict in my *doodies*, taking every responsibility to heart.

Security Guard

One of my primary responsibilities is to guard my yard, and I take it very seriously. After I joined the team, my humans had the area behind the house fenced in—not as a toilet but as a playpen. That distinction is emphasized because I prefer to expel my business during our walks so as not to sully my most beloved domain. On the rare occasion, I may release something in an emergency, but I let my humans know where it is and they remove it promptly. They are well trained and were already yard broken when I arrived.

Our house is a very, very, very fine house... with NO cats in the yard!

I also guard the house because it is my castle. And since we don't have a moat, it's all down to me.

Customs Officer

Everything that comes through the door has to pass through customs, which consists of my nose. I am the *scent*inal. Shoes off, bags inspected, contents sniffed, certain items confiscated, bodies examined. If dogs have been encountered, the process takes twice as long because there are so many interesting scents to process. (I never advertise the fact that, during all of this, I'm also searching for anything that may have been acquired specifically for me.)

Fitness Instructor

When dogs and humans merge their lives, it is important to consider things like energy level, physical fitness, physical ability, and one's general notion of motion. Everyone should be on the same page as far as minimum exercise requirements. Believe me— I'm not complaining. But it turns out my humans need to be walked a lot! Furthermore, they get so excited to go on a walk, but once outside they just can't keep up.

I often wonder if my humans' slow pace is because they don't have the same motivation as I do. (I wait for the walk to go to the bathroom, whereas they go to the bathroom right before the walk. I just can't get these two housebroken. To this day they continue to go indoors. They even have a ROOM for it!) Back to the walk...I often hear people call out, "Who's walking whom?!" And I think, "That's silly. Isn't it obvious?" Yes, sometimes I have to pull them, but to be fair, I have four legs and they each only have two. It stands to reason that they are only going half my speed.

I walk my humans every day, without fail, in any weather. I'm surprised they didn't name me Jim. I mean, Gym.

The walks are good for me too. I'm always *doodie-full*, and afterwards I am always pooped.

Between the two, Dad is far more fit than Mom. He's up for anything, and I definitely take advantage of it. With Mom, I have to be a little more patient. She can manage well enough; she's always good to go in cold weather, and I've successfully increased her arm strength. But she falters in the heat, and she lacks the endurance that we boys enjoy. (I don't mean all boys; that would be sexist. I mean we boys, specifically me and Dad.)

Funny story! I've pulled Mom down on the ground more times than I can count. She's pretty resilient, always bouncing back up and soldiering on. We play very rough, and she's always covered in bruises and scratches. You know how it is. So, get this. One day we're walking through the woods, I've got Dad on the leash so Mom could roam a bit. Big mistake. What does she do? Falls over a downed tree and breaks her ankle! Poor thing! Of course I didn't WANT her to be hurt. But, man, I laughed my ass off. One of the funniest things I've ever seen. And I could enjoy it fully because it had nothing to do with me! We left her laying there in the woods, just as it was getting dark; I brought Dad to the car to get me settled, then he went back to get her. He said she was dragging along the path like an injured moth. We drove all the way home with her ankle in the cooler... sorry, I'm laughing again! Hold on, she's giving me the evil eye.

Phew! Good times. Anyway, a lot of what followed wasn't so funny for any of us. Her recovery was a real drag. (Some other time I'll tell you about my torn cruciate ligament, subsequent surgery, and resulting rehab. Totally different recovery, because I had THREE other legs!) I think she might have faired better if she'd gone around on all fours, but humans are very stubborn. She insisted on staying upright. I'm still a little pissed off that she wasn't subjected to that abhorrent cone (like I was), but hey, good for her. She had enough problems.

After that, for months, I only had to walk one of my humans. I guess it was a "break" for me too! Dad was such a good sport, though; he took care of everything and STILL came along for his walks every day. During that time, I offered re*PEET*Adly to just go by myself so he could stay home with Mom, but he was determined to be

67

on the other end of that leash. What a guy!

I am not ashamed to say that I kick dirt. I kick a lot of dirt. Grass, leaves, and pebbles too. If it's behind me when I gear up, it's going airborne. In fact, there has been some speculation as to whether or not I could be leased out as a tiller. Anyway, if Mom is behind me and Dad on a walk... target practice! I'll fake another pee just so I can look convincing when I rotate and send the earth in her direction. As she mumbles her disapproval, Dad and I make eye contact. *Bull's*-eye!

Oh, crap...now she knows. Never mind; it had a good run. (Ah, she's smiling while typing. All is right with the world.)

Bodyguard

As a bodyguard, I make sure people think twice before approaching my humans. Unfortunately, this has morphed into protecting them from people they also love. Oops. (Turns out, I'm very possessive.)

I have also developed skills for guarding the mind. Mom is an introvert, so on our walks I act as the ultimate buffer. This is a new kind of running for me—running interference.

I suggested that we put a sign on the door that says, "Beware of Owner," but for some reason Dad thinks that could cause trouble...

Bouncer

As a *bone*-a fide bouncer, I fulfill two roles. I am the Class A Security Guard (as described earlier), making sure that no individual without an invitation can gain access to the castle grounds. I get such a kick out of it, watching people on the street register what I'm telling them. To date, nobody has so much as attempted to dispute this with me. I hope to keep it that way.

The other part of being a bouncer is, in fact, bouncing. Do you remember earlier when I referred to body slamming? Well, here's how it goes. I run full speed at my humans. When I'm about three feet from one of them, I hurl my body into the air straight at them. They have learned to brace themselves for impact, upon which I bounce off, spin in the air, and land on all fours. This has often resulted in them falling to the ground, even Dad! It is utterly hysterical. For them? Not so much.

But in typical quirky human fashion, they never actually move out of the way. I do believe they are worried I will hurt MYSELF if they don't curtail my aerial mobility. Again, utterly hysterical those two.

Entertainer

First, let's address wag levels as entertainment.

The low-level wag is used when guilt is involved.

The mid-level wag is the most common. It can go on for quite some time, and usually represents the ultimate joy of the humans returning home. A butt wiggle sends it right over the top.

The high-level wag is excitedly asking what is going to happen next.

The flat, drumming wag happens in one's sleep. A true crowd pleaser. (Or so I'm told.)

Then, there's singing. Never under-estimate the power of song, especial-ly mine. My humans will stop dead in their tracks. Every time.

As for random antics, if I do something that makes my humans laugh, I add it to my repertoire. For example, since I am of medium height, when I walk around their bed with my tail in the air, my tail is all they can see. So, instead of just jumping up in the bed with them, I circle the bed repeatedly until one of them, in their best JAWS voice, yells "SHARK! SHARK!" Mission accomplished—they start laughing, I jump up, and we all go to sleep happy. (Please note that although I am of medium height, I do possess the strength of a much larger dog. Just sayin'.)

Moral Compass

My humans know to follow my lead.

Security Blanket

For Mom. Every. Single. Night.

Antidepressant

It seems that all I have to do is snuggle up close, and any existing demons just fly out the window. Moods change, nerves relax, anxiety dissipates, and Snow Dog defeats ByTor every time.

Muse

It has been said that I am, perhaps, a muse.

My humans have said that I am definitely a muse.

A*muse*ING!

Exfoliant

Remember that first kiss that Mom didn't get to see? Not to worry. As it happens, I can't hold my *licker*, and her face is my favorite flavor. Every day we have a face-off.

Environmentalist

These days you hear a lot about every human's carbon footprint. Since it sounds quite harmful to the environment, I suggest that humans just STOP stepping in carbon. The bigger the foot, the more substantial the damage, I'm guessing.

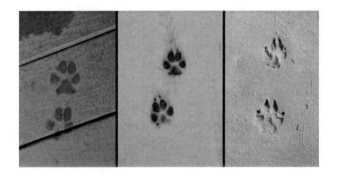

What's worse is I found out recently that dogs have a carbon footprint too. This information is completely baffling, as all my paw prints are natural, and I waste no money or resources on shoes of any kind. Could it be that they have us confused with horses? I've heard horses wear shoes. And horses are bigger. Yeah, that's it. And we all know that horses consume more meat than dogs do. Uh oh—that can't be right. Can I back out now before I incriminate myself further?

Best Friend

I've heard it said that Dog is Man's Best Friend. But I always wondered, "WHICH man?!" It's quite a sweeping statement. But having witnessed the worst (and now the best) in human behavior, I get it. Never ever did I think I would be ANY man's best friend, but then I found Dad. Mystery solved.

Happy Hoarder

It really was an adjustment to go from having nothing to having everything. Let's be honest, unlike dogs, humans are way too hung up on possessions. But now I have to admit that when it comes to toys, I have become the Happy Hoarder. Sometimes I play until I fall asleep in them, or I fall asleep with one in my mouth.

Life Coach

I know my humans respect how I handle life, and they try to follow suit. Really, they do. Every day I set a good example for them, and it's fascinating to watch them process my enlightened approach to our experiences. They try so hard to emulate me that I almost can't find it in my heart to discipline them. There are times, though, when they just aren't getting it, and their frustration and disappointment seem overwhelming. When this happens, I have a trick to snap them out of it—I do something naughty on purpose, then give them my forgive-me-I-know-not-what-I-do look. For some reason, this role reversal causes sheer delight and sets everything straight again. They believe it's their function to discipline ME, which I must say is very endearing. Dad is actually really good at it, but Mom undoes everything. I have her wrapped around my dewclaw.

I've learned to accept Mom and Dad's flaws. They're only human, after all. But I wonder…since next year is 2020, does that mean all humans will experience an improved level of perception? With *20/20 vision*? (Yes, I'm wagging my tail at my own joke!)

CHAPTER EIGHT:
PAWS FOR THOUGHT

So there you have it. As a member of the Bullied Breed, I would like to advocate for any dog who is branded with a bad reputation through no fault of their own. For many Pit Bulls, the stigma is just the final scar. As if they haven't suffered enough already.

Please remember that behind every Pit Bull's face and form is a soul who was once a puppy. An innocent puppy who knew no evil...until evil was forced upon them. Then all they knew was survival. Humans often say that life is what you make it, but unfortunately dogs don't have that option. If they're lucky, someone will come along and make their life worth living.

Thank you, Mom and Dad. My bowl runneth over.

And yet, I must confess—even with all the blessings that have been bestowed upon me, I often revert to the original joy of chasing my tail. But ultimately, aren't we all just chasing the end of our tale?

I hope you've enjoyed my story. If I have the opportunity to write another book it will be a study on the quirkiness and insanity of humanity. Dogs are best prepared if they can learn to interpret the world through their human's eyes. It's an acquired skill, but once learned, it makes life a lot easier. And remember—be patient. Humans really need our help. We must teach them to slow down and live in the moment.

Feel free to visit me on Facebook—my page is PeetaBred. (The dog doesn't have to be pure bred, but the advice should be.) I'll be there, getting completely confused between that "page" and this book. Why is it that my book has pages, but my page has posts? Whatever.

The Dude Abides.

(I can't drink a White Russian, so I just pretend to be one.)

ACKNOWLEDGMENTS

Mom and Dad

They are credited on the title page as co-author and collaborator because it was only fair that I throw them a bone. In reality, they were no more than a glorified assistant (Mom) and a critic (Dad). I don't mind setting this record straight because the true credit goes to all their love.

Val Cervarich – Writing Help KC

Val's editing was in-*val*-uable.

(Sorry I didn't tell you about her, Mom; I didn't want to hurt your feelings.)

Ted Ehlers and Mia – Good Dog!! Positive Training, LLC

Jenna Teti and Reuben – Think Smart Dog Training

These talented teams are gifted with the patience of saints. Just thinking of them makes me happy. Eternal love.

Peggy Steinhilber, Geoff Fallows, and Jesse Tucci – PetSpa of Little Ferry, NJ

They do grooming and boarding. I didn't go for the grooming, but I stayed for the hospitality! Utterly delightful.

ACKNOWLEDGMENTS

Becky Livingston – Owner Penheel Marketing

Thank you for recognizing my intellectual potential.

Dr. Shannon Foy – Brentwood Veterinary Center, Wilson, NC

She may be the only one who knows what happened to my balls.

Zarina Mak and Michelle Zelazny – See Spot Rescued, Jersey City, NJ

Thank you for bridging the gap until Mom and Dad came along. Eternal thanks.

Dr. Lawrence Buchholz, Adam K., and Staff – Animal Clinic & Hospital of Jersey City, NJ

Not that I enjoy visiting you, but you guys rock!

Dr. Katharine Salmeri – Red Bank Veterinary Hospital, Tinton Falls, NJ

Bless you for my bionic knee and full mobility. But with all due respect, I hope I never *knee*d you again.

ABOUT THE AUTHOR

Really?

What more could you possibly want to know?

If you'd like a signature, send me your dog-eared copy of this book, and I will promptly step in mud and paw the title page.

THANK YOU FOR READING MY BOOK!

I always welcome feeding…I mean feed-back, and I'd love to hear what you have to say.

I need your input to make my next book better!

Please leave me a review on Amazon and let me know your thoughts.

Much appreciated!

Peeta Foy Schalhoub

Made in United States
North Haven, CT
26 December 2021

13699106R00062